D1170479

HE IS THE MOST DANGEROUS LIVING BEING ON THE FACE OF THE EARTH!
THOUGH CONSIDERED A MENACE T SOCIETY, HE WAS INSTRUMENTAL I THE FOUNDING OF THE AVENGERS EARTH'S MIGHTIEST HEROES!
...OR BOTH? THESE ARE QUESTIONS WE WILL ATTEMPT TO ANSWER TONIGHT...
HOW CAN THEY CALL THE AVENGERS "EARTH'S MIGHTIEST," WHEN THEIR ROSTER DOESN'T INCLUDE--?
HI, HONEY! I'M HOME...

...MISS ME?
SILLY QUESTION! OF COURSE, I MISSED YOU!

YOU'RE HOME EARLY. HOW WAS WORK?
PUT OUT A FIRE IN BOSTON...
...STOPPED A TORNADO IN IOWA. NICE, SLOW DAY.

MORE ABOUT DOCTOR ROBERT BRUCE BANNER--
LEGACY
--AND THE CURSE OF THE INCREDIBLE HULK--

--WHEN LEGACY CONTINUES.
I WISH I COULD HAVE DONE MORE FOR BANNER BACK THEN...
OH, CLARK! WHEN YOU FIRST MET THE HULK, NO ONE SUSPECTED THAT HE WAS DOCTOR BANNER.

JUST AS NO ONE HAS ANY REASON TO BELIEVE THAT SUPERMAN HAS ANOTHER IDENTITY!
OTHERWISE, THESE SPECS WOULD NEVER WORK AS A DISGUISE.
GOOD POINT.

STILL, BANNER AND I HAD MORE IN COMMON THAN EITHER OF US REALIZED. WE BOTH LED DOUBLE LIVES--
--AND WE WERE BOTH IRREVOCABLY CHANGED BY EXPLOSIONS! SO MUCH ALIKE...

...AND YET, SO DIFFERENT. THE FORCES THAT BLASTED KRYPTON APART DESTROYED THE PLANET OF MY ANCESTORS. I WOULD HAVE DIED THERE AS WELL, HAD MY FATHER NOT SENT ME TO EARTH.
THANKS TO HIS FORESIGHT, I GREW STRONG AND POWERFUL UNDER THE RAYS OF EARTH'S YELLOW SUN. LITERALLY, YOU COULD SAY I WAS BORN UNDER A LUCKY STAR.

DOCTOR BANNER WAS NEVER THAT FORTUNATE, AS WE KNOW NOW. IT'S IRONIC...
"...LIKE MY FATHER JOR-EL, BANNER WAS RUSHING TO SAVE A LIFE WHEN HE WAS CAUGHT ON THE EDGE OF A THERMONUCLEAR EXPLOSION! BY RIGHTS, THE RADIATION SHOULD HAVE KILLED HIM...

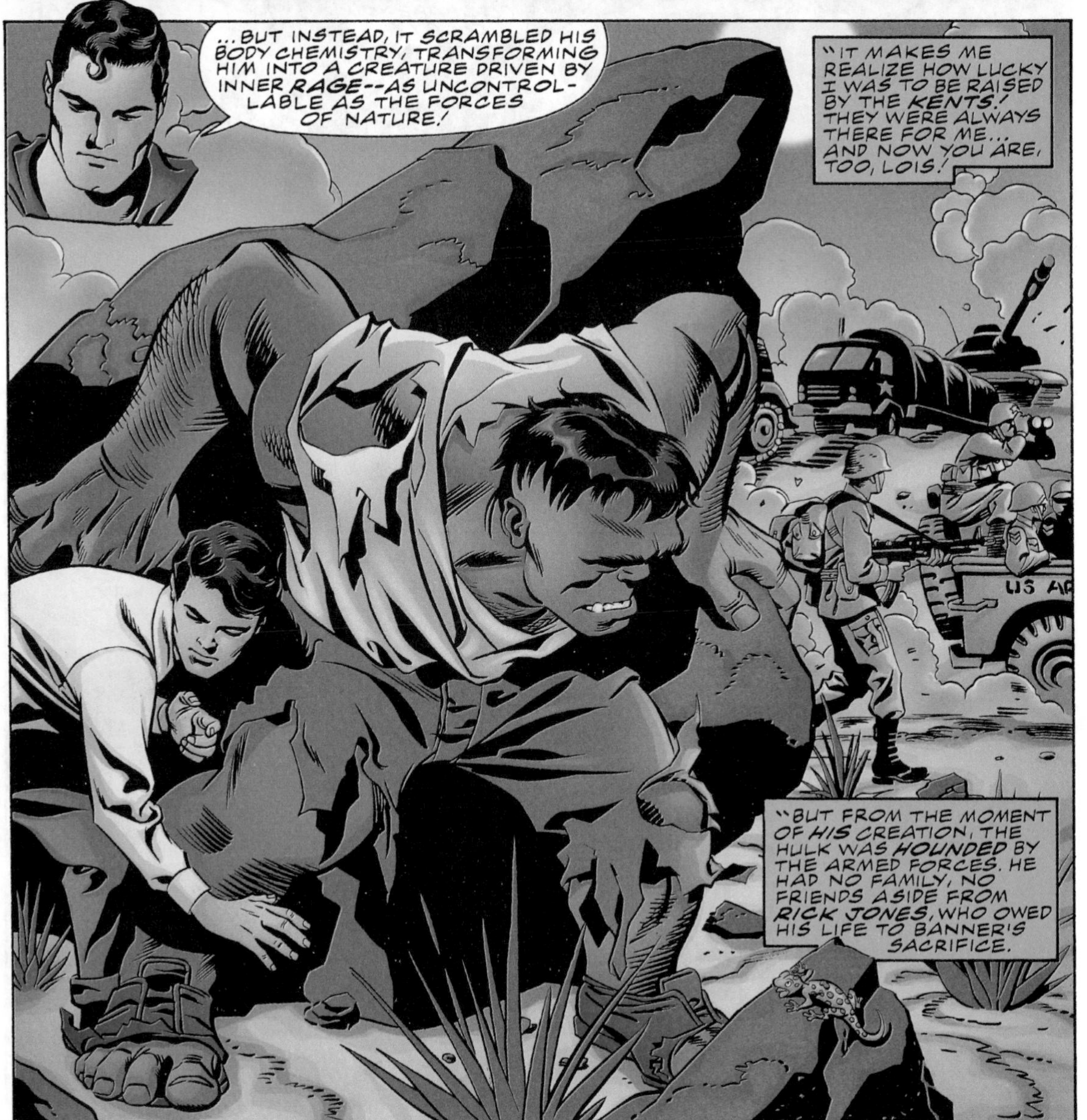
...BUT INSTEAD, IT SCRAMBLED HIS BODY CHEMISTRY, TRANSFORMING HIM INTO A CREATURE DRIVEN BY INNER RAGE--AS UNCONTROLLABLE AS THE FORCES OF NATURE!
"IT MAKES ME REALIZE HOW LUCKY I WAS TO BE RAISED BY THE KENTS! THEY WERE ALWAYS THERE FOR ME... AND NOW YOU ARE, TOO, LOIS!
"BUT FROM THE MOMENT OF HIS CREATION, THE HULK WAS HOUNDED BY THE ARMED FORCES. HE HAD NO FAMILY, NO FRIENDS ASIDE FROM RICK JONES, WHO OWED HIS LIFE TO BANNER'S SACRIFICE.

"I CAN'T BEGIN TO IMAGINE WHAT LIFE MUST HAVE BEEN LIKE FOR BANNER...
...ALL THOSE YEARS AGO

NO! NO!!

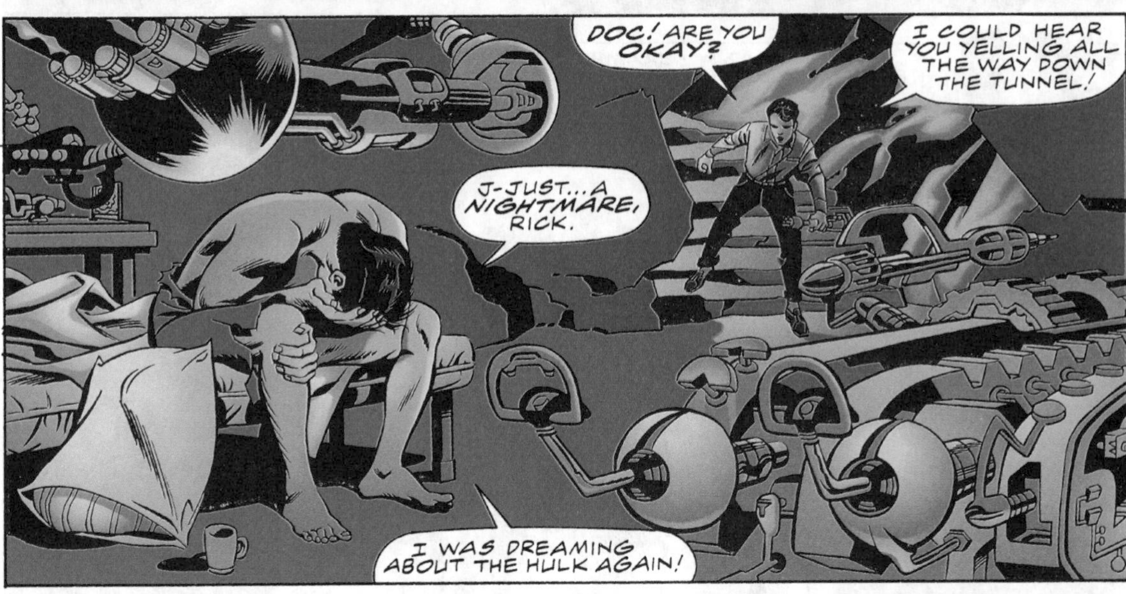
DOC! ARE YOU OKAY?
I COULD HEAR YOU YELLING ALL THE WAY DOWN THE TUNNEL!
J-JUST...A NIGHTMARE, RICK.
I WAS DREAMING ABOUT THE HULK AGAIN!

HE WAS AFTER ME! IT WAS SO VIVID! SO TERRIFYING!
GOT MY HEART POUNDING--!
HEY, IT'S OKAY...
...WE'VE GOT THE HULK UNDER CONTROL NOW, RIGHT?
I...

ANYWAY, I GOT THIS GIZMO YOU WERE USING TO STUDY OL'...
...GREEN-SKIN?
OUT OF MY WAY!!

I DON'T BELIEVE THIS! DOC HASN'T CHANGED SPONTANEOUSLY TO THE HULK IN MONTHS! AND EVEN WHEN HE DID, IT WAS NEVER IN THE DAYTIME!
DOC--WAIT UP!
DON'T CALL ME "DOC"! THAT'S WHAT YOU CALL THAT PUNY BANNER!

I'M THE HULK!
HULK--RIGHT! I CAN DIG IT!
LISTEN, MAYBE WE SHOULD GET YOU BACK DOWN INTO YOUR LAB AND--!
NOT MY LAB! BANNER'S!

AND I'M SICK OF BEING BANNER!
WHUUGH!

HULK--STOP!!
NO!
NOBODY TELLS THE HULK WHAT TO DO!!

HULK--!
OH, MAN! THIS IS BAD!

SIMULTANEOUSLY, AT A LARGE MIDWESTERN UNIVERSITY...
I HEAR YOU'VE MADE QUITE A BREAKTHROUGH, PROFESSOR CARSON!
YES, MR. KENT... ONE THAT MAY BE A BOON TO HUMANITY...

...MY NEW TRIANGULATING SEISMOGRAPH SHOULD ENABLE US TO PREDICT EARTHQUAKES BEFORE THEY HAPPEN!
HOW DOES IT WORK?
BASICALLY, IT DETECTS THE MOST MINUTE SEISMIC CHANGES, PINPOINTING THEIR LOCATION AND ...WHAT'S THIS?
SOMETHING WRONG?

I'M NOT CERTAIN. THE SCANNER INDICATES A WHOLE SERIES OF MINI-TREMORS--ONE JOLT AFTER ANOTHER--
ZZZK ZZZK
--MOVING ACROSS SOUTHERN NEW MEXICO--TOWARDS THE ARIZONA BORDER! I'VE NEVER SEEN SUCH READINGS--!

PROFESSOR--GET BACK!
SKZZTT
BOOOM
WHA--?!

M-MY THANKS, MR. KENT!
OBVIOUSLY, MY MECHANISM NEEDS FURTHER TESTING.
CAN'T IMAGINE WHAT MADE IT MALFUNCTION LIKE THAT.

NEITHER CAN I, PROFESSOR. BUT IF THERE WAS ANYTHING TO THOSE READINGS--
--THEN SUPERMAN MAY BE NEEDED...
2-B

"...IN ARIZONA!!"
OTIS SEZ TRAVELERS Welcome
OTIS' GENERAL STOR
COME AND GIT IT!
ICE
♫OH, I GOT YER DRUMSTICK, I GOT YER WING...
...I GOT YER CHICKEN, FIT FER A KING!♫
DON'T BE SHY! COME AN' GIT IT!
FOOD!
BOOM
GREAT DAY IN TH' MORNIN'! WHU...

...WHAT DO YOU CALL THAT?!
UH?

HUNGRY!

PARDNER, IT'S ALL YERS!

OH, LORDY! WHUT IF THAT DON'T FILL 'IM UP?
LOOK--

"--UP YONDER!"
AH! NOW ALL THE SEISMIC PHENOMENA ADDS UP!
THE HULK, I PRESUME! DID THEY RUN OUT OF PLATES?
Mmmph? WHO ARE YOU SUPPOSED TO BE?
THEY CALL ME SUPERMAN!
SUPERMAN!
HE WAS FLYIN', I TELL YA!
HEARD ABOUT 'IM ON TV!
A REAL HERO--!
HE'LL SAVE US!

SO YOU'RE THE BIG SHOT FROM BACK EAST, HUH?
WELL, I WOULDN'T SAY THAT--!

NEITHER WOULD I!
MAN OF STEEL-- BIG DEAL!!
I SAVED THE WHOLE WORLD FROM THE METAL MASTER, BUT DOES ANYONE CARE?!
WHOA! TAKE IT EASY, BIG--

--FELLA?
DON'T TELL ME WHAT TO DO!!

KTOOM
TOOM
TOOM

I'VE BEEN THROUGH HURRICANES THAT DIDN'T HIT THAT HARD!

TIME TO LAY DOWN THE LAW!
OKAY, BIG GREEN-- LET'S HOLD IT RIGHT THERE, SHALL WE?
BTOK
LET GO!

WOW! HE'S NOT--
--ONLY BIG--
--HE'S FAST!
AND STRONG! STRONGER THAN ANYONE I'VE EVER GONE UP AGAINST!

IF HE CAN DO THIS TO ME...

...THE PEOPLE BACK AT THAT BARBECUE DON'T STAND A CHANCE!

SUPER-MAN!
THE HULK-- WHERE IS HE?!
I SEEN HIM! HE GRABBED THE REST OF THE FOOD AND JUMPED OFF OVER THOSE HILLS!
'SOKAY, HON! THE BAD GREEN MAN IS GONE!
OH, HONEY, YOU SURE?
YAY!
TOLD YA HE'D BE BACK!
SON, THAT'S THE CONTINENTAL DIVIDE!

NO SIGN OF THAT MONSTER--AND HIGH WINDS HAVE ALREADY OBSCURED HIS HEAT TRAIL. AS FAST AS HE IS, HE COULD BE ANYWHERE BY NOW!
I'LL GIVE THE ROCKIES A FLY-BY, BUT SOMETHING TELLS ME I'LL HAVE BETTER LUCK LOCATING THE HULK...
...FROM THE VANTAGE OF METROPOLIS!
HMM...

...KENT'S HAD HIS NOSE TO THE SCREEN EVER SINCE HE GOT BACK FROM THE MIDWEST. HE'S ONTO SOMETHING--!
LAS CRUCES SUN--"BREAK-IN AT AIR BASE" ...EL PASO TIMES--"HULK RIPS THROUGH CIRCUS" ...CARLSBAD BULLETIN--"CREATURE WRECKS BURNING HOUSE"...
PACKERS TAKE NFC CHAMPIONSHIP
...THERE'S A DEFINITE PATTERN HERE!

RESEARCHING THE HULK, IS HE?
WELL, WE'LL SEE ABOUT THAT!
KENT BEAT ME TO THE FIRST SUPERMAN EXCLUSIVE --AND NOW HE'S GOING AFTER THE HULK!

CHIEF, I HAVE A MONSTER IDEA FOR A NEW EXPOSE!
GO AHEAD, LOIS. I'M LISTENING...

WHAT?!? YOU ASSIGNED LOIS TO INVESTIGATE THE HULK?!

MR. WHITE, I WANTED THAT STORY! I'VE BEEN CHASING DOWN LEADS ALL DAY!
SORRY, KENT, BUT YOU SHOULD HAVE SPOKEN UP SOONER.
LOIS GOT HER BID IN FIRST. SHE'S PROBABLY HALFWAY TO NEW MEXICO BY NOW.

I NEEDED THAT ASSIGNMENT AS COVER, WHILE I TRACKED THE HULK DOWN AS SUPERMAN...!
WELL, CHIEF... HOW ABOUT MY EXPANDING THE SEISMOLOGIST STORY INTO A SERIES... SAY ON AMERICA'S NEW SCIENTISTS?!
I'D SAY YOU NEED A HOOK...
...SOMETHING TO MAKE THE PUBLIC WANT TO READ IT!

IF I WENT WEST TO INTERVIEW DOCTOR BRUCE BANNER, WE COULD TIE IT INTO LOIS'S HULK STORY! BANNER WAS ONCE ASSIGNED TO HELP TRACK THE MONSTER DOWN...
...AND HIS PROFILE COULD LAUNCH THE SERIES --YES! NOW THAT'S A HOOK! GET ON IT, KENT!
ON MY WAY, CHIEF...
"...I'LL BE IN NEW MEXICO BEFORE YOU KNOW IT!"
AS I UNDERSTAND IT, SHERIFF, YOU WERE STILL A DEPUTY WHEN YOU ENCOUNTERED THE HULK?
THAT'S CORRECT, MS. LANE. IN FACT, THAT INCIDENT GOT ME THIS JOB!
LAST ELECTION, EVERYBODY WANTED TO VOTE FOR "THE MAN WHO STOOD UP TO THE HULK"!

HARD TO BEAT A SLOGAN LIKE THAT!
WAS THERE ANYTHING UNUSUAL ABOUT THAT ENCOUNTER...?
MA'AM, EVERYTHING'S UNUSUAL WHERE THE HULK'S CONCERNED.
SHERIFF
I WAS THE FIRST TO RESPOND TO A REPORTED HOUSE FIRE. WHEN I ARRIVED, THE FIRE WAS OUT. SEEMS THE HULK HAD TORN AWAY THE SIDE OF THE BUILDING THAT WAS BURNING.
DIDN'T KNOW THAT AT THE TIME, THOUGH. JUST SAW THAT BIG GREEN CUSS AND OPENED FIRE.
SHERIFF
GLAD I MISSED, NOW. HE HAD SOME TEENAGE BOY WITH HIM...
THAT'S RIGHT, MS. LANE...
...A YOUNG MAN TIPPED US OFF THAT THE RINGMASTER HAD CAPTURED THE HULK...THOUGH HE DIDN'T STAY A CAPTIVE FOR LONG.
"THE BUREAU OWES A DEBT OF GRATITUDE TO--"

RICK JONES? YES, MA'AM!
WE TOOK HIM INTO CUSTODY UNDER ORDERS FROM GENERAL ROSS. I DON'T RECALL THE CHARGES... DOESN'T MATTER ANYWAY, THEY WERE LATER DROPPED.
"IT WAS THE HULK WHO FREED HIM! ONLY TIME I EVER LOST A PRISONER."
MP
RESTRICTED
ARMY

RICK? HE'S SO COOL! HE'S THE ONE WHO ORGANIZED OUR HAM RADIO NETWORK!
DIDJA KNOW WE HELPED THE HULK DEFEAT THE METAL MASTER?! IT'S TRUE!
"OUR TEEN BRIGADE GOT THE STUFF THE HULK NEEDED TO TURN THE TABLE ON THAT FLYIN' WEIRDO! BUT WE NEVER COULDA DONE IT WITHOUT RICK!"

A DOZEN DIFFERENT INTERVIEWS AND NO TWO OF THEM SAY THE SAME THING ABOUT THE HULK...
...BUT THEY ALL MENTION THIS RICK JONES!
MAYBE IF I CAN FIND HIM...!
COME ON, HULK, WHERE ARE YA?
'S BEEN DAYS SINCE--!

WAIT A MINUTE! THERE HE IS!
NOW...IF DOC'S GIZMO WORKS LIKE I HOPE--!
WOW! SURE LOOKS LIKE THE REAL THING! BUT DOES THE HULK SEE IT?
YES! HE'S COMING IN! HE...

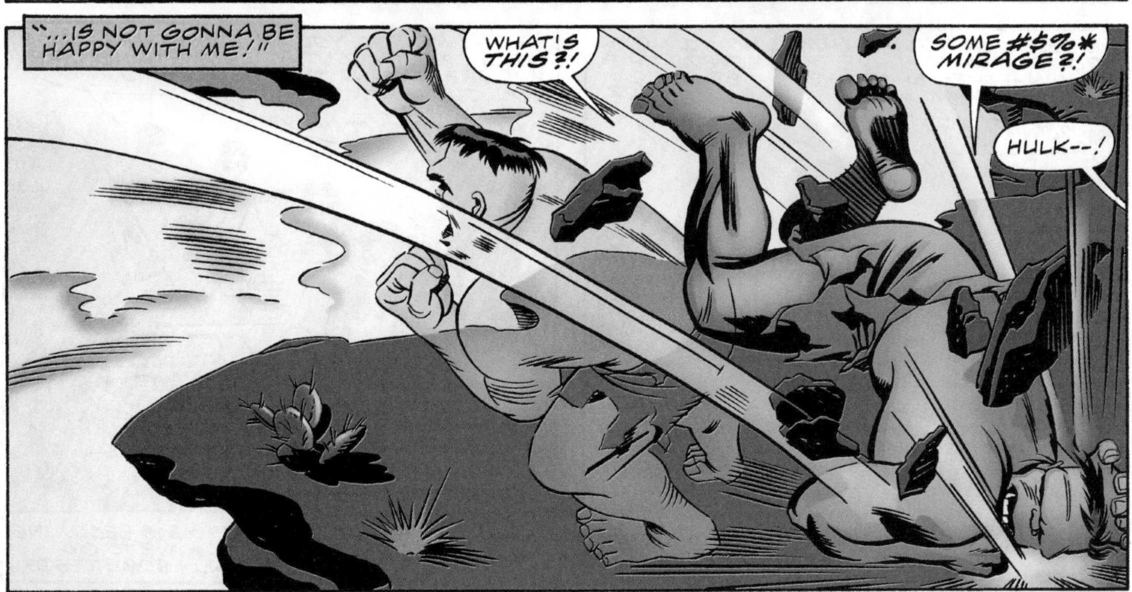
"...IS NOT GONNA BE HAPPY WITH ME!"
WHAT'S THIS?!
SOME #$%* MIRAGE?!
HULK--!

YOU! MIGHT'VE KNOWN IT WAS YOU!
YEAH. SORRY.

SORRY?!?
DOWN THE HATCH!

≡GLK!≡ TRYIN' TO POISON ME, KID? I...

...I OUGHT TO... TO...

...UUGHN... I...
WHAT...?
R-RICK...?

TAKE IT EASY, DOC. HERE...GOT YOUR SPECS FOR YA!
H-HOW--?

I USED YOUR HOLOGRAM PROJECTOR TO LURE THE HULK IN--THEN SHOT ONE OF YOUR SPECIAL TRANQUILIZERS DOWN HIS THROAT.
NO... I MEAN, HOW DID THIS EPISODE BEGIN?

YA GOT ME, DOC. YOU WERE UPSET ABOUT A BAD DREAM, AND THEN YOU JUST SORTA... I DUNNO... "HULKED OUT!"
I WAS AFRAID OF SOMETHING LIKE THIS.
JONZ
THE HULK SIDE OF ME IS BECOMING STRONGER, RICK. I HAVE TO GO BACK TO THE CAVE. RUN SOME TESTS...

'FRAID THAT'LL HAVE TO WAIT, DOC! THUNDER-BOLT ROSS HAS BEEN BURNING UP THE PHONE LINES LOOKING FOR YOU!
SOME BIGWIG FROM BACK EAST FLEW OUT TO MEET YOU--AND T-BOLT WANTS YOU AT THE BASE PRONTO!
BUT--!
'SOKAY, THERE'S A CHANGE OF CLOTHES BEHIND THE SEAT.

G77-B3
HERE YA GO, DOC! YOU NEED ME FOR ANYTHING ELSE, JUST GIVE A CALL! YOU GOT MY NUMBER!
THANKS, RICK... FOR THE LIFT, FOR ...EVERYTHING.
HEY, NO PROBLEM! AFTER ALL, I OWE YOU!

DOCTOR BANNER--?
YES?

THIS IS AN *HONOR*, SIR. I'M CLARK KENT-- FROM THE *METROPOLIS DAILY PLANET*. I'D LIKE TO SPEAK WITH YOU ABOUT YOUR WORK.
ALL RIGHT, MR. KENT...

...BUT I MUST TELL YOU, I'M NOT INTERESTED IN PERSONAL CELEBRITY.
I QUITE UNDERSTAND. YOU SEE, I'M WRITING A SERIES AIMED AT ENCOURAGING INTEREST IN THE SCIENCES AND...
BANNER!!

?
WHERE IN THE SAM HILL HAVE YOU *BEEN*?!
C-CONDUCTING... FIELD STUDIES, GENERAL. SORRY IF--!
BAD ENOUGH, HOSTING CORPORATE V.I.P.S--

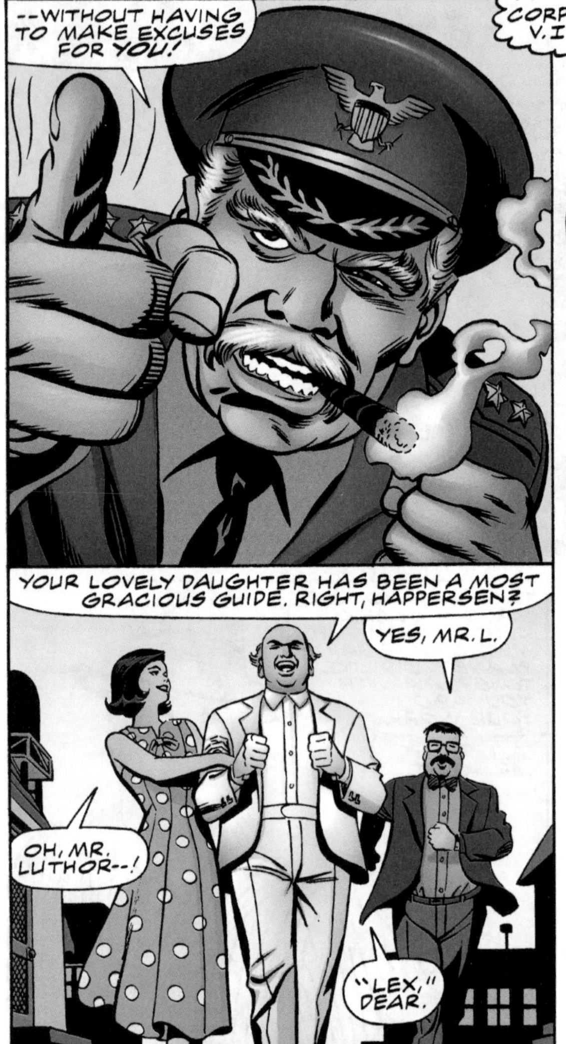
--WITHOUT HAVING TO MAKE EXCUSES FOR YOU!

CORPORATE V.I.P.S?
WELL... HELLO, KENT.
GENERAL ROSS, IS THAT OUR ERRANT GENIUS?
YES. SORRY TO HAVE KEPT YOU WAITING!
NO APOLOGIES NEEDED, SIR. NONE AT ALL!

YOUR LOVELY DAUGHTER HAS BEEN A MOST GRACIOUS GUIDE. RIGHT, HAPPERSEN?
YES, MR. L.
OH, MR. LUTHOR--!
"LEX," DEAR.
LEX, THIS IS--!
DR. BANNER! AT LEXCORP, WE'VE FOLLOWED YOUR CAREER WITH GREAT INTEREST! WHY, SIR, YOU'RE LIKE EINSTEIN, OPPENHEIMER, AND TELLER--ALL ROLLED INTO ONE!
THAT'S VERY FLATTERING, BUT I'M HARDLY--!
WE HAVE SO MUCH TO TALK ABOUT!

YOU'LL EXCUSE US, WON'T YOU, GENERAL?
I'M PARTICULARLY INTRIGUED BY YOUR GAMMA RAY RESEARCH...

BLASTED INDUSTRIALISTS... ALWAYS TRYING TO WALTZ OFF WITH MY SCIENTISTS! IF HE DIDN'T HAVE CLEARANCE--!
LUTHOR ONCE SWORE HE'D DESTROY SUPERMAN. WHAT'S HE UP TO HERE? NOW?

MEANWHILE...
DRIVE-IN
SO, POLLY... WHATCHA UP TO THIS WEEKEND?
GOTTA WORK. I'M SAVIN' UP FOR SPRING BREAK.
SODA~ICE CR
WHAT CAN I GET YA?

COUPLE'A CHILI DOGS, FRIES, AND A LARGE CHERRY SODER!

OKAY, YA KNOW... I AM OFF TOMORROW NIGHT!
YEAH? WELL...
PARDON ME--

--I'M LOOKING FOR RICK JONES! KNOW WHERE I CAN FIND HIM?

RIGHT HERE, SWEET THING! RICHARD M. JONES, AT YOUR SERVICE!
AND YOU ARE--?
LOIS...

...LOIS LANE. I'M A REPORTER AND I'D LIKE TO ASK YOU A FEW QUESTIONS ABOUT THE HULK! FROM WHAT I'VE HEARD, YOU TWO MUST BE GOOD FRIENDS!
F-FRIENDS? WITH THE HULK? L-LADY, YOU GOTTA BE KIDDIN'!

HEY, LOOK AT THE TIME!
SORRY! GOTTA RUN!
JONES!!
I'VE SPENT 36 HOURS TRACKING YOU DOWN! THIS ISN'T OVER YET!

HI. COULD I GET A ROOT BEER FLOAT? WITH EXTRA ICE CREAM?
S-S-SURE.
SUPER-MAN?! WHAT ARE YOU DOING HERE?!
GETTING SOMETHING TO DRINK. FLYING IS THIRSTY WORK!

OH, YOU MEAN WHY AM I IN NEW MEXICO?
SAME AS YOU-- GETTING A LINE ON THE HULK!
HOW DID YOU KNOW--?
RAN INTO CLARK KENT UP THE ROAD. HE TOLD ME.

KENT?! WHAT'S HE DOING HERE?!?
INTERVIEWING SOME SCIENTIST. OH, AND DID YOU KNOW LEX LUTHOR'S IN TOWN?
ON THE HOUSE, SUPERMAN!
THANKS!

DID ALL OF METROPOLIS FOLLOW ME OUT HERE?! WHAT'S LUTHOR UP TO?!
FRANKLY --MMPH-- I'M NOT CERTAIN...
IT'S HIM, I TELL YA! IT'S REALLY HIM!

...BUT I HOPE TO FIND OUT!
YOU WOULD TELL ME IF YOU UNCOVERED ANY-THING--WOULDN'T YOU, LOIS?

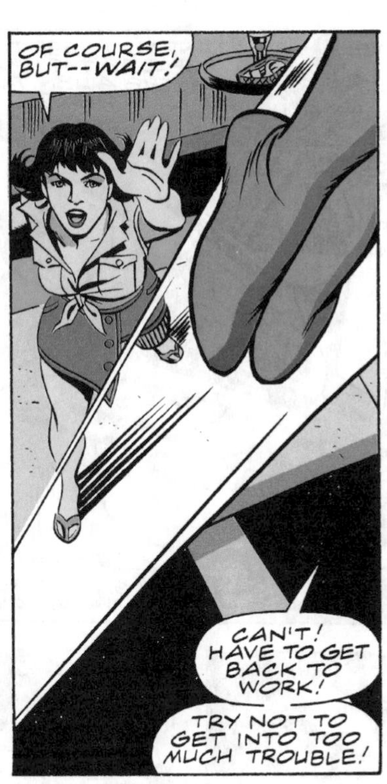
OF COURSE, BUT--WAIT!
CAN'T! HAVE TO GET BACK TO WORK!
TRY NOT TO GET INTO TOO MUCH TROUBLE!

OOOO, MEN!
I'LL GET TO THE BOTTOM OF THIS, IF IT'S THE LAST THING I DO!

EASY TO SEE HOW LUTHOR AND HIS TECH-ADVISOR GAINED ADMITTANCE TO THE BASE--LEXCORP WAS THE MAJOR CONTRACTOR FOR MOST OF THEIR ARMAMENT.
I'D LOVE TO KNOW WHAT THEY'RE UP TO...
...BUT, UNFORTUNATELY, THE BUNKER THAT BANNER TOOK THEM IN-TO IS SO HEAVILY SHIELDED, MY X-RAY VISION IS BLOCKED! I CAN'T SEE ANYTHING THAT MIGHT BE GOING ON--
G
STOR

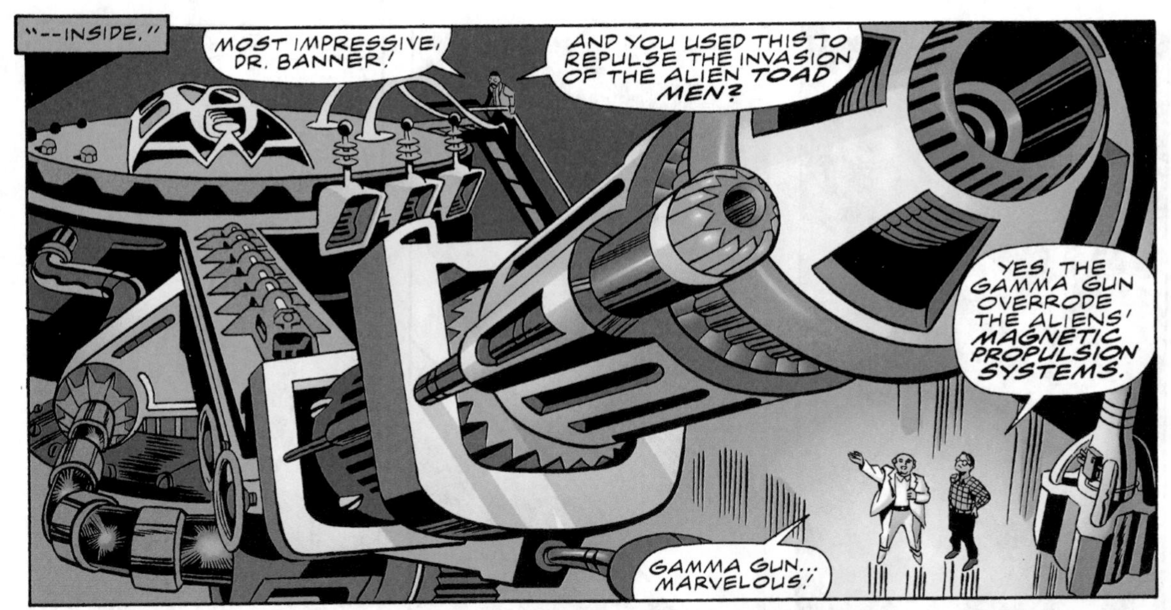
"--INSIDE."
MOST IMPRESSIVE, DR. BANNER!
AND YOU USED THIS TO REPULSE THE INVASION OF THE ALIEN TOAD MEN?
YES, THE GAMMA GUN OVERRODE THE ALIENS' MAGNETIC PROPULSION SYSTEMS.
GAMMA GUN... MARVELOUS!

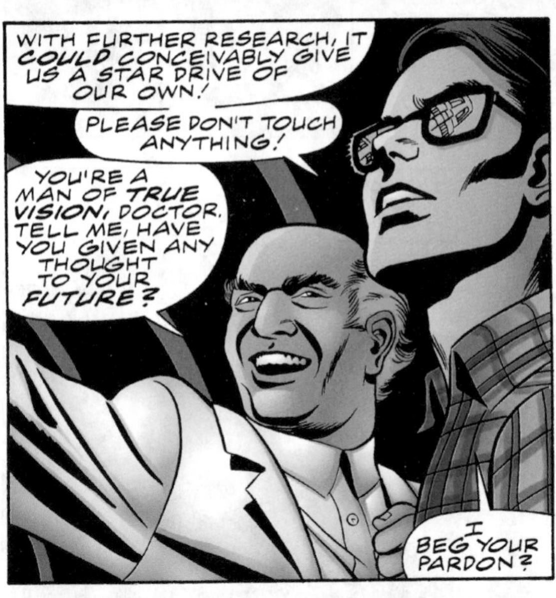
WITH FURTHER RESEARCH, IT COULD CONCEIVABLY GIVE US A STAR DRIVE OF OUR OWN!
PLEASE DON'T TOUCH ANYTHING!
YOU'RE A MAN OF TRUE VISION, DOCTOR. TELL ME, HAVE YOU GIVEN ANY THOUGHT TO YOUR FUTURE?
I BEG YOUR PARDON?

I'M ALWAYS SEEKING OUT GREAT MINDS FOR LEXCORP'S RESEARCH DIVISION. I OFFER MUCH MORE GENEROUS COMPENSATION--AND FAR BETTER PERKS--THAN THE GOVERNMENT!
WELL...
RING RING
EXCUSE ME... MY PHONE!

BANNER HERE... RICK? WHA--?
SLOW DOWN! WHAT'S WRONG?

I JUST GOT THE THIRD DEGREE FROM A SNOOPY REPORTER... ASKING ABOUT THE HULK!
REALLY? ODD...
...I SPOKE EARLIER WITH A REPORTER MYSELF!
??? WHERE'S BETTY GOING WITH LUTHOR?

NO, I DON'T KNOW THAT THERE'S A CONNECTION, BUT WE SHOULD BE CAUTIOUS JUST THE SAME.
WHAT IS LUTHOR UP TO?
LISTEN, THINGS ARE VERY BUSY RIGHT NOW. WE'LL TALK LATER.
B. BANNER

GOT TO CATCH UP TO--!
OH! S-SORRY KENT!
QUITE ALL RIGHT, DOCTOR! SHOULD'VE WATCHED WHERE I WAS GOING!
1B
HAVE YOU SEEN BETTY...MS. ROSS? I THOUGHT I SAW HER--!

SHE AND HER FATHER WERE WITH LUTHOR--BUT I BELIEVE THEY'VE GONE THEIR SEPARATE WAYS.
LUTHOR JUST LEFT WITH HIS ADVISOR...

I MANAGED TO GET PHOTOS OF THE GAMMA GUN'S CONTROL SURFACES, MR. L.!
GOOD.
NEXT, HAPPERSEN, THERE'S CERTAIN ITEMS YOU MUST PROCURE...WHILE I WINE AND DINE BANNER AND THE ROSSES.

I WANT TO GET A LEAD ON WHAT MAY BE THE DOCTOR'S GREATEST CREATION!
THE HULK, SIR?!
YES. I SUSPECT THAT ONE OF BANNER'S EXPERIMENTS CREATED THE MONSTER...OR BROUGHT IT TO EARTH. WHATEVER...

...IF I CAN GET THE HULK'S STRENGTH AND BANNER'S GENIUS AT MY BECK AND CALL--
--SUPERMAN WILL BE DOOMED!

I'M GLAD I COULD TALK YOU INTO AN INTERVIEW, DOCTOR. QUITE A SET-UP YOU HAVE HERE!
MM-HM.
YOU'LL PARDON ME WHILE I CHECK ON A FEW THINGS, KENT. FEEL FREE TO LOOK AROUND... JUST DON'T TOUCH ANYTHING.
CERTAINLY. I WAS WONDERING...
...IF WE MIGHT DISCUSS YOUR EFFORTS TO TRACK DOWN THE HULK.
OH, THAT ALL ENDED WHEN THE HULK WAS PARDONED FOR HELPING STOP THE METAL MASTER.

I... SEE.
NO SHIELDING HERE... FILES LOOK VERY INTERESTING.
WELL, CAN YOU TELL ME WHAT YOU THINK HIS ORIGINS ARE?

I... I WOULDN'T EVEN HAZARD A GUESS, KENT.
TOO BAD. DID YOU KNOW--
--THAT THE HULK RECENTLY ATTACKED SUPERMAN?
THE FIGHT ENDED BEFORE ANYONE WAS HURT...

...BUT DOZENS OF LIVES WERE PUT AT RISK BY--!
DR. BANNER? ARE YOU ALL RIGHT?
JUST... A MUSCLE SPASM, AND A BIT... OF A MIGRAINE. C-COULD WE CONTINUE THIS ANOTHER TIME?

OF COURSE. I'LL BE IN TOUCH.
EXIT
MUST-CALM-DOWN.
MUSTN'T-LET-HULK-OUT.

KENT IS RIGHT... THE HULK REMAINS A THREAT. I MUST KEEP MY EMOTIONS IN CHECK.
OTHERWISE, I RISK RELEASING...

"...AN UNCONTROLLABLE MONSTER!"
THAT NEURON-MAGNET WAS SPECIALLY DESIGNED TO ATTRACT AND HOLD LIVING BEINGS.
MY ENGINEERS TELL ME THAT THE HULK EXERTED A FORCE IN EXCESS OF 25 TONS AGAINST THOSE BARS!

HE WAS FREE IN 40 SECONDS!
BETTY--?
HOW RUDE OF ME! I SHOULD HAVE REALIZED ...YOU'VE HAD SOME FRIGHTENING ENCOUNTERS WITH THE HULK YOURSELF, HAVENT YOU?
YES.
JUST A FEW MORE MINUTES, BETTY. WE'RE ALMOST THROUGH!

AND NOW THEY'VE PARDONED THAT MENACE!
GENERAL, THE HULK HAS DONE SOME GOOD.
YES, AND THINK WHAT MIGHT BE ACCOMPLISHED IF WE COULD BUT HARNESS HIS POWER-- EH, BANNER?

NO ONE WOULD EVER NEED FEAR HIM AGAIN.
LOOK AT THAT SLEAZE...!

I SHOULD INTERVIEW BETTY ROSS... TO WARN HER AWAY FROM LUTHOR, IF NOTHING ELSE!
I KNOW TOO WELL HOW EASY IT IS...

"...TO BE TAKEN IN BY HIS CHARM!"
THANK YOU SO MUCH FOR VISITING MY LITTLE HACIENDA!
WONDERFUL TIME!
SEE YOU SOON!

HAPPERSEN?! REPORT!
EVERY-THING'S IN PLACE, MR. L...

..."OPERATION DECOY" IS READY TO GO. BUT WE MUST EXERCISE CAUTION. BOTH LOIS LANE AND SUPERMAN HAVE BEEN SEEN IN THE AREA!
WHAT?!

FIRST, KENT--AND NOW LANE AND SUPERMAN? INTERESTING!
BUT, JUST MORE CHESS PIECES FOR THE BOARD!

BANNER IS OBVIOUSLY ATTRACTED TO BETTY... SHE WILL BE THE TOOL BY WHICH I GAIN CON-TROL OVER HIM... AND PERHAPS THE HULK, AS WELL.

THE NEXT DAY...
BETTY ROSS?
I'M LOIS LANE OF THE DAILY PLANET. CAN WE TALK?

SOON...
REALLY, MS. LANE! YOU MAKE LEX SOUND LIKE ...SOME MONSTER!
LET'S JUST SAY HE'S FAR FROM PERFECT. BUT SINCE YOU MENTIONED MONSTERS, WHAT CAN YOU TELL ME ABOUT THE HULK? YOU'VE SEEN HIM--?
SEEN HIM?! HE ONCE TOOK ME HOSTAGE! THE HULK IS HUGE... TERRIFYING! AND YET...

...HE NEVER REALLY TRIED TO HARM ME. THERE WAS A STRANGE SADNESS ABOUT HIM.
OF COURSE, MY FATHER DESPISES HIM. JUST THE THOUGHT OF THE HULK RUNNING FREE SETS HIM OFF.
I KNOW THAT REACTION! MY FATHER WAS ARMY-- A CAREER OFFICER-- AND HE--!

WHAT ON EARTH--?!
IT'S JUST A DUST DEVIL! WE GET THEM ALL THE TIME!

MORE LIKE A MINI-TWISTER!
IT IS UNUSUALLY INTENSE. MUST BE A STORM ON THE WAY!

THAT'S NO STORM! THERE'S SOMETHING IN THERE!
GOOD LORD... IS THAT...?!

THE HULK!
"REALLY, MR. KENT...

...THE TIME I SPENT TRACKING THE HULK WAS ONLY A *MINUSCULE* FRACTION OF MY RESEARCH.
I KNOW, DOCTOR. BUT IT'S THE SIDE OF YOUR WORK THAT WILL ATTRACT THE READERS--

--THE *HOOK* THAT MAKES THEM WANT TO READ ABOUT THE SCIENCE INVOLVED.
BUT THAT DUTY WAS HARDLY GLAMOROUS. I MYSELF NEVER EVEN *SAW* THE HULK. I HAD TO RELY UPON IMAGES CAPTURED BY REMOTE CAMERAS.
ALL RIGHT, THEN; LET'S TALK ABOUT YOUR WORK ON THE *G-BOMB*.

I WISH YOU WOULDN'T CALL IT THAT.
IT WAS A FUSION DEVICE CREATED FOR A STRATEGIC DEFENSE PROJECT. DEVELOPING OFFENSIVE WEAPONS WAS NEVER MY INTENT.
BUT SURELY YOU REALIZE THE *DEADLY POTENTIAL* OF YOUR CREATIONS...?

YES. YES, I DO...

...IT'S SOMETHING I MUST LIVE WITH EVERY WAKING MOMENT.
KENT...IF I TOLD YOU SOMETHING IN CONFIDENCE...

...COULD YOU KEEP IT SECRET?
DOCTOR, YOU'D BE SURPRISED AT THE SECRETS I'VE KEPT. I...
EXCUSE ME. MY CELL PHONE--!
BRRT-BRRT

LOIS? WHAT'S UP?
OH, NOT MUCH! MY RENTAL CAR'S A PANCAKE AND MY INTERVIEWEE'S BEEN ABDUCTED!
WHAT?!? WHERE ARE YOU?! ARE YOU ALL RIGHT?!
I'M OKAY. IT ALL HAPPENED SO SUDDENLY! THIS... MONSTER CAME AT US OUT OF A SANDSTORM! IT HAD TO HAVE BEEN THE HULK!
IF YOU SEE SUPERMAN BEFORE I DO, TELL HIM...

THE HULK HAS KIDNAPPED BETTY ROSS!
WHAT?!? BUT THAT CAN'T BE!

I'M AFRAID IT IS!
I HAVE TO GO!
O-OF COURSE.

DOCTOR! HAVE YOU HEARD THE TERRIBLE NEWS--?
YES! CAN'T TALK NOW!

RICK! THANK HEAVENS!
NEED A LIFT, DOC?

YES. STEP ON IT!

HAH-HA! YES, DOCTOR! RUN AS FAST AS YOU CAN!
I'LL BE RIGHT BEHIND!

SAY AGAIN, CAR-THREE?
CANCEL THAT SECOND WRECKER, DISPATCH... OTHER HELP HAS ARRIVED.
NO LEADS FROM THE CAR... NOT EVEN OVERSIZED FINGERPRINTS!
ALL SET TO ROLL!
THANKS AGAIN, SUPERMAN! WE'D'VE BEEN HOURS SCRAPIN' THAT ALL TOGETHER!
IT'S LUCKY KENT WAS ABLE TO REACH YOU--!

LOIS, YOU'RE LUCKY TO BE ALIVE! THE HULK IS CAPABLE OF ANYTHING!
TELL ME ABOUT IT. CAN YOU STOP HIM?

I INTEND TO TRY!
I SEE A HEAT TRAIL HEADING WEST. THAT'S MY BEST LEAD.

YOU'RE NOT GOING TO LEAVE ME HERE!
STAY WITH THE DEPUTIES, LOIS--

"--THIS IS A JOB FOR SUPERMAN!"
THE POLICE SCANNER'S ALL LIT UP OVER THIS, DOC. I DON'T GET IT-- HOW COULD ANYONE IMPERSONATE THE HULK?!
I... DON'T KNOW, RICK...

I BET IT'S A SET UP! YOU GONNA LIE-LOW IN THE CAVE--
--OR USE YOUR G-RAY TO CHANGE AND--?

NO NEED... FOR THAT!
UH...

HULK--!
OH, MAN--
THAT WAS A
NEW TIRE!
NO ONE PASSES HIMSELF OFF AS ME AND GETS AWAY WITH IT!!
BLAM
SCREEEEEE
JONZ

I SURE WOULDN'T WANT TO BE THAT FAKE HULK!
"FORGET ABOUT TAILING BANNER, HAPPERSEN--

"--LOW ALTITUDE SCANS HAVE LOCATED THE HULK! LURE HIM IN!"
"YESSIR, MR. L! GUIDANCE LASER IS LOCKING ON...

EH?
"...I THINK WE GOT HIS ATTENTION!"

BETTY!
"YES! HE'S DEFINITELY SIGHTED THE DECOY!"

GET AWAY FROM HER!
THOOM

NO. GIRL BELONGS TO HULK NOW.

I AM THE HULK!

BTAMM
"LOOK AT HIM, HAPPERSEN! WHAT A MAGNIFICENT BRUTE...

...HE'S EVERYTHING I'D HOPED FOR--AND MORE!
B-BUT, MR. L...THAT ROBOT COST MILLIONS! A-AND HE'S TEARING IT TO PIECES! HOW ARE WE EVER GOING TO RESTRAIN HIM?!
YOU DON'T HOLD BACK SUCH RAGE, SYDNEY--YOU FAN IT TO WHITE-HOT INTENSITY, THEN GIVE IT A TARGET! SPEAKING OF WHOM...

...WHERE'S SUPER-MAN?
IMAGING RADAR SHOWS HIM HALF-WAY ALONG THE TRAIL WE LAID--AND PICKING UP SPEED!
PERFECT! BY THE TIME HE GETS THERE--

"--THE HULK WILL HAVE DISPOSED OF HIS FIRST 'SPARRING PARTNER,' AND EVERYTHING WILL BE SET UP...
SKATOOM

"...FOR THE TITLE BOUT!"
THERE HE IS!
MUST GET HIM AWAY FROM THE WOMAN!
HER LIFE DEPENDS ON ME!

HE'S SPOTTED ME! GOT TO HIT HIM FAST--
?!
--AND HIT HIM HARD!

BOOM BOOM BOOM BOOM

UNGH...?
STILL AWAKE?
NOT FOR LONG!
I LEARNED MY LESSON LAST TIME!
GIVE MY REGARDS TO THE NEXT COUNTY!
WOKT
WAKT
WUKT
WAKT
WOKT
MS. ROSS? DON'T WORRY, I'M SUPERMAN! I'VE REMOVED THE HULK--!
THE HULK...?
HE KIDNAPPED YOU--!
NO...I WAS GRABBED BY ...METAL... SOME SORT OF...
ROBOT!
I WAS IN SUCH A HURRY, I NEVER NOTICED...
SOMEONE'S PLAYING GAMES WITH US.
BUT... WHO...?

WUP-WUP-WUP-WUP-WUP
LET ME WORRY ABOUT THAT.
I DON'T SEE ANY BROKEN BONES...HOW DO YOU FEEL?
A LITTLE LIGHT-HEADED.
I MUST CATCH UP TO THE HULK AND MAKE AMENDS BEFORE THIS ESCALATES ANY FURTHER.
MEDIC! DOWN HERE!
MAKE AMENDS? WITH THE HULK?!
I KNOW. IT WON'T BE EASY --ESPECIALLY NOW!--BUT I HAVE TO TRY...
GOOD LUCK.
$#*#% IF I EVER LAY EYES ON THAT MISERABLE--!
ALL RIGHT, SUPERMAN, LET'S SEE HOW YOU LIKE A LITTLE OF YOUR OWN MEDICINE!
EH? BACK FOR MORE?
HULK! WE'VE BEEN SET UP! LET'S TALK TRUCE!
I'LL SHOW YOU A TRUCE--!

BRROOMM
THUNDER, SIR?
NO, IT'S THE HULK! AND... SUPERMAN?!

MOVE OUT! ALL UNITS, PROCEED TO SECTOR 7-- AND PREPARE TO FIRE ON MY COMMAND!

SIR? WHAT ABOUT SUPERMAN?
SUPPOSED TO BE BULLET-PROOF, ISN'T HE?

HE'D BETTER LIVE UP TO HIS REP-- BECAUSE WE'RE BRINGING THAT MONSTER DOWN!
FIRE!!
G-77

BADOOM
BDOOM
DOOM
GOT 'IM!

HOLD YOUR FIRE! LOOKS LIKE...
UH-OH.

THOOM
INCOMING!!

THAT...ACTUALLY CAME CLOSE TO KNOCKING THE WIND OUT OF ME.
DO I DARE HOPE THE HULK TOOK IT HARDER?

MISSILES?! I HATE MISSILES!!
NO... NO SUCH LUCK.
X-4

SEE HOW YOU LIKE THEM!!
EVERY-BODY-- CLEAR OUT!

GOOD THING NONE OF THESE ARE HEAT-SEEKERS!
A LITTLE APPLIED HEAT VISION SHOULD FUSE THEIR IMPACT DETONATORS AND RENDER THEM INERT!

HULK-- I'VE BEEN TRYING TO TELL YOU-- WE'VE BOTH BEEN SET UP!
BUT IF YOU WON'T LISTEN--!

GET THE INJURED BACK TO BASE!
GENERAL! TH-THEY'RE PUNCHING EACH OTHER INTO THE FOOTHILLS!
I HAVE EYES, SOLDIER!
SIR! CIVILIAN VEHICLE APPROACHING!

LUTHOR?! GET OUT OF HERE! THIS IS A COMBAT ZONE!
I CAN HELP, GENERAL!
IS THAT SO? A HUNDRED SPECIALLY TRAINED MEN WITH THE LATEST ORDNANCE DIDN'T EVEN SLOW THOSE TWO POWERHOUSES DOWN!

YOU HAVE NOTHING THAT COULD DO BETTER!
IT'S NOT WHAT I HAVE, IT'S WHAT YOU HAVE!
TWO WORDS, ROSS-- GAMMA GUN!

GOT TO WATCH MYSELF...
...MY LAST PUNCH DROVE HIM HALFWAY DOWN INTO THAT MOUNTAIN! I'M NOT USED TO LETTING GO LIKE THIS!

HULK! ARE YOU ALL RIGHT? I KNOW YOU'RE NOT TO BLAME FOR THIS!
CAN YOU HEAR ME? LET'S TALK--!

BOOMMMM

DID YOU THINK A FEW TONS OF ROCK COULD STOP ME?!
NOTHING CAN STOP THE HULK!! NOTHING!

IF IT COULD STOP AN ALIEN ARMADA, IT CAN STOP THE HULK!
BUT BANNER'S NOWHERE TO BE FOUND! WITHOUT HIM TO CALIBRATE IT--!

HAPPERSEN CAN DO THAT! HE STUDIED THE CON-TROLS...UNDER BANNER'S SUPERVISION!
WHAT ABOUT SUPERMAN? CONVENTIONAL WEAPONRY IS ONE THING, BUT THIS--!

SUPERMAN? I'M SURE HE CAN... TAKE A LITTLE HEAT.
THIS WEAPON COST BILLIONS, LUTHOR!
AND WHAT'S IT WORTH TO YOU TO DESTROY THE HULK?

LOCKED ON TARGETS, MR. L-- ALL SYS-TEMS GO!
WELL, GENERAL...?
ALL RIGHT... FIRE!

INSTANTLY, OVER A MILE AWAY...
YEAAGH! WHAT--?!

BANNER'S... GAMMA GUN! BUT... CAN'T BE BANNER--!
LUTHOR?
LUTHOR! MUST BE!
TOLD YOU... WE WERE BOTH... SET UP! HE'D DO ANYTHING... TO KILL ME!

THEN HE'S A FOOL! I KNOW... FROM BANNER'S WEAPONS! WE'LL BE JUST... THE FIRST VICTIMS!
IT COULD KILL... EVERY-THING... WITHIN 500 MILES!

THEN... WE MUST... STOP IT!
I'M WITH YOU!
THINK THERE'S... A PITCH LEFT... IN YOUR THROWING ARM?
LET'S SEE...

NEVER FELT... SUCH PAIN! NEVER! BUT I'VE--
--GOT--TO BUILD UP SPEED! GOT TO--
--THROW THE HULK FREE!!

MR. L, THE CORE'S OVER-HEATING!
BETTER CUT BACK!

DON'T YOU DARE!
I WANT MORE POWER! MORE!

ARE YOU CRAZY?! INDICATORS ARE ALL RED!
SHUT IT DOWN, OR--!

SKRAZZKT
I'M SHUTTING YOU DOWN, LUTHOR!! NOW--AND FOREVER!!!

MISTER LUTHORRR--!!
ATTENTION! THIS IS A PRIORITY ALERT!
EVACUATE THE BASE--ON THE DOUBLE! THIS IS NOT A DRILL!
SHIELD ME, SYDNEY!

WOOP! WOOP-WOOP WOOOP! WOOOP!
=HUFF= ESTIMATE =HUFF= 15 SECONDS =HUFF= TO DETONATION!
LUTHOR, SO HELP ME, IF WE LIVE THROUGH THIS--!
IT WASN'T MY FAULT! THE HULK--!

THE HULK... YES. IF WE DIE, AT LEAST HE WILL, TOO!
FORGET THAT! RUN!!
5 SECONDS!

GOING SOMEWHERE, GENTLEMEN?
UUFF!!
WUHH--!
SUPERMAN! WE'VE GOT TO GET TO COVER!
NO...

WHOOMPF
...WE'RE SAFE ENOUGH HERE! THE HULK ALREADY TOOK OUT THE WORST OF IT!
HE MAY HAVE JUST SACRIFICED HIMSELF TO SAVE US ALL!

UNHAND ME, YOU RECKLESS--!
I'M RECKLESS? YOU'RE THE ONE WHO CAUSED ALL THIS!

THAT'S PREPOSTEROUS! THE HULK--!
THE HULK IS NO INNOCENT, BUT SOMEONE INCITED HIM...
...AND I'M BEGINNING TO UNDERSTAND HIS ANGER!

HOLEE--! THAT'S THE BUNKER WITH DOC'S GAMMA GUN!
JONZ

COULD EVEN THE HULK SURVIVE THAT?!

IF NOT FOR HIM, I'D BE DEAD! IF NOT FOR ME...!
DON'T COUNT ME OUT JUST YET, RICK.

DOC! YOU'RE ALIVE!
THANKS TO THE HULK. HE FORCED OPEN THE EMERGENCY ACCESS TUNNEL, JUST BEFORE THE GAMMA CORE WENT UP. THE ENERGY RELEASE CHANGED ME BACK--
--AND BOUNCED ME OFF A FEW WALLS. DO YOU HAVE MY GLASSES?
RIGHT HERE, DOC!

MAN, YOU SHOULD'VE SEEN THE EXPLOSION FROM OUT HERE! WHAT A RUSH!
NO DOUBT! FROM WHAT I CAN RECALL, THE HULK ENJOYED THAT JOB! THAT, AND FINDING--

"--AN ALLY!"
LOOK FAMILIAR, LOIS?
THE HULK WAS A ROBOT?!

ONLY THE ONE THAT STOPPED YOU...
...THE GENUINE ARTICLE DESTROYED THE GAMMA GUN! I'M AFRAID THERE'S BEEN NO SIGN OF HIM IN THE WRECKAGE...
SO WHO BUILT THIS ROBOT?

IT'S A MODIFIED VERSION OF A MODEL USED IN TESTING ANTI-HULK WEAPONRY--BUILT FOR THE ARMED FORCES BY LEXCORP!
I DON'T SUPPOSE YOU KNOW ANYTHING ABOUT THIS, LEX?

CERTAINLY NOT! AND I RESENT THE IMPLICATION!
I'M RETURNING TO METROPOLIS NOW TO LAUNCH A FULL INVESTIGATION INTO THE MATTER! AND I WON'T REST UNTIL I FIND THE PARTIES RESPONSIBLE!

YES. I'M SURE YOU WON'T.
A ROBOT? THEN IT WASN'T THE HULK WHO--?
NO, DADDY!

IN FACT, SUPERMAN THINKS THE HULK PROBABLY SAVED ME FROM THE ROBOT.
HAS THE WHOLE WORLD GONE CRAZY?!
BETTY!

BRUCE! ARE YOU ALL RIGHT? I WAS SO WORRIED ABOUT YOU!
REALLY? ME, TOO! ABOUT YOU, I MEAN!

OH, BUT, BRUCE ...YOUR GAMMA GUN! YOU PUT SO MUCH WORK INTO IT!
IT'S ALL RIGHT. I'LL DESIGN SOME-THING BETTER, SOME-THING... SAFER.

CLOSE... I CAME SO CLOSE, HAPPERSEN!
BUT YOU LEARNED A LOT, SIR... FOR NEXT TIME!
YES, YOU'RE RIGHT...

...WE MUST BEEF UP OUR RESEARCH AND DEVELOPMENT DIVISION!
ONE WAY OR ANOTHER, I'LL FIND A WAY TO DESTROY SUPERMAN!

THE NEXT DAY...
HOT OFF THE PRESSES, KENT! READ IT AND WEEP!
AND WHY WOULD I DO THAT, LOIS?
DAILY PLANET
SUPERMAN VS THE HULK
PACKERS TAKE NFC CHAMPIONSHIP
BABE HITS 714

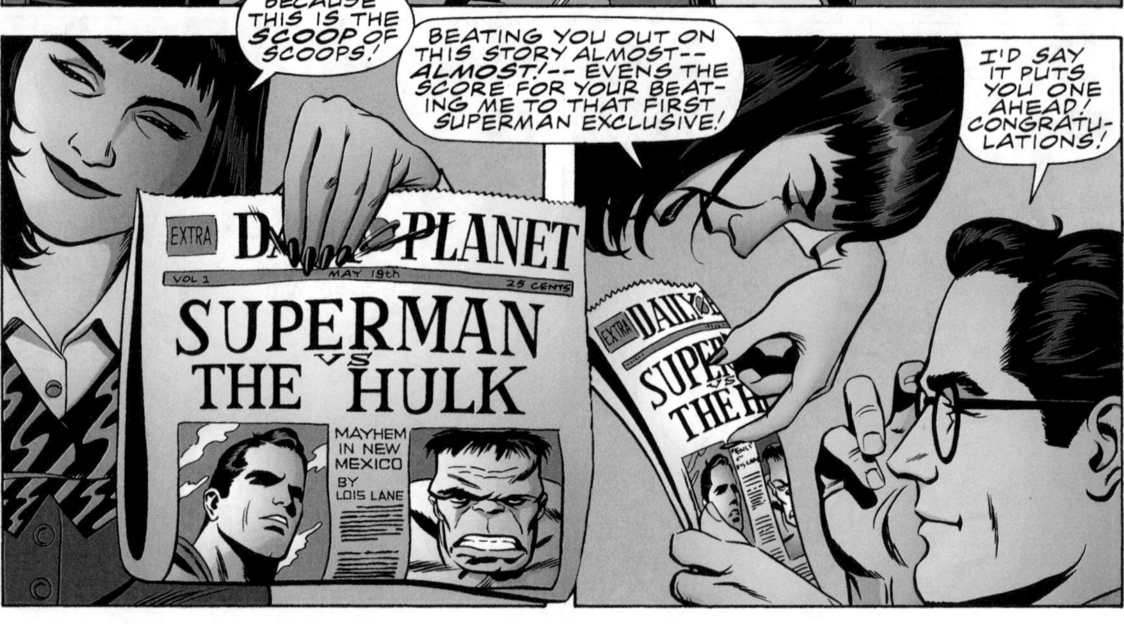
BECAUSE THIS IS THE SCOOP OF SCOOPS!
BEATING YOU OUT ON THIS STORY ALMOST-- ALMOST!-- EVENS THE SCORE FOR YOUR BEATING ME TO THAT FIRST SUPERMAN EXCLUSIVE!
I'D SAY IT PUTS YOU ONE AHEAD! CONGRATULATIONS!
EXTRA
PLANET
VOL 1
MAY 19th
25 CENTS
SUPERMAN VS THE HULK
MAYHEM IN NEW MEXICO
BY LOIS LANE

OF COURSE, WE STILL DON'T KNOW WHERE THE HULK CAME FROM. NOW THAT HE'S GONE, WE MAY NEVER KNOW.
IS HE GONE, LOIS? I WONDER...
LOOKING BACK, IT'S ALL SO OBVIOUS! POOR BANNER...

...HE ENDURED SUCH HELL IN BOTH OF HIS IDENTITIES. AND THE NIGHTMARE ONLY GOT WORSE WHEN HIS SECRET BECAME PUBLIC KNOWLEDGE!
I CERTAINLY REMEMBER HOW SURPRISED I WAS! AND YET... AFTER ALL THAT ...HE AND BETTY MARRIED!
SHE MUST HAVE LOVED HIM VERY, VERY MUCH.
IT'S SO SAD... THE WAY IT ENDED...

...AFTER ALL THEY WENT THROUGH, THEY DESERVED BETTER.
IT MAKES ME REALIZE, ALL OVER AGAIN, HOW LUCKY WE ARE...
YES.

I WONDER WHERE BANNER IS NOW... HOW HE'S HOLDING UP?

...WEDDING PHOTOS SHOW THEM BOTH SMILING BRAVELY, BUT IN HER BOOK, FIELD OF GREEN, BETTY ROSS BANNER TOLD OF HER FATHER'S VIOLENT OPPOSITION TO THE MARRIAGE.
CERTAINLY, THE CURSE OF THE HULK CONTINUED TO HAUNT THE YOUNG COUPLE. AND ANY HOPES OF HAPPINESS ENDED TRAGICALLY--

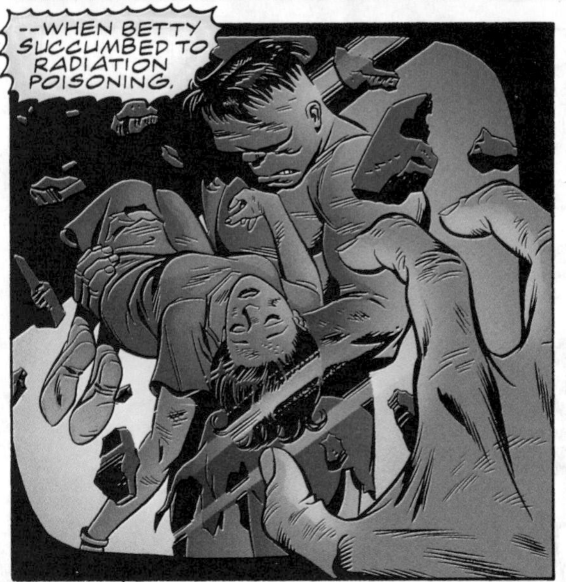
--WHEN BETTY SUCCUMBED TO RADIATION POISONING.

HER DEATH HAD A PROFOUND EFFECT ON BANNER--AND ON THE HULK AS WELL.
IT IS RUMORED THAT BOTH SUFFERED A SEVERE EMOTIONAL BREAKDOWN.

AND THOUGH THE CURRENT WHEREABOUTS OF DOCTOR ROBERT BRUCE BANNER ARE UNKNOWN, SPORADIC SIGHTINGS OF A GREEN-SKINNED MAN-MONSTER ARE EVIDENCE THAT HE STILL LIVES--
--AND THAT THE STORY OF THE INCREDIBLE HULK HAS YET TO REACH ITS END!